ABCmouse.com
Early Learning Academy

People and Places

ABCmouse.com *Early Learning Academy* is the award-winning digital learning program that covers math, reading, science, social studies, art, music, and more for kids ages 2 to 8.

With more than 10,000 individual Learning Activities and over 850 lessons across 10 levels, ABCmouse is a proven educational resource that is trusted by parents and teachers across the U.S. and around the world.

Go to
www.ABCmouse.com
to learn more.

ABC Mouse

ABCmouse.com

At-Home
LEARNING TIPS ☑

Dear Families,

The keys to successfully managing a "learn-at-home" situation are often related to time and space. Here are a few tips to ensure that you and your child are getting the most of your opportunities to learn at home.

Managing Time

☐ Establish a routine for your day. For example, plan to start "learning time" at the same time every day, and schedule consistent breaks for meals, exercise, and free time. Make that routine as similar to your child's school day as possible.

☐ Set goals for how much time to spend on each learning activity, such as reading silently for 20 minutes. Be sure to celebrate when goals are achieved.

☐ Plan ahead for when you need time for yourself. Explain when that will be, and help your child use a clock to know when that time is over.

☐ Include your child in planning out how to spend your time. Children are much more likely to stick with a plan when they had a part in deciding what it is.

Managing Space

☐ Identify one or more "learning spaces" around your home. Pick places that are as comfortable and distraction-free as possible.

☐ Use headphones to cancel out noise when it's not possible to create a distraction-free space.

☐ Collect containers such as shoeboxes or small cubbies to hold school items.

☐ Choose one area of the house to store school items when not in use. Having a dedicated place to "turn in" and "pick up" items helps keep things organized.

☐ Allow children to use outdoor spaces when possible. Outdoor spaces provide fresh air and can help lift moods. They can also provide fantastic learning opportunities themselves!

☐ Just like with the last note about time, include your child in planning out how to use your space, too.

—Team ABCmouse

Baker

Draw yourself and a friend here.

What do bakers use?

mixing bowl

whisk

spoon

What do bakers use?

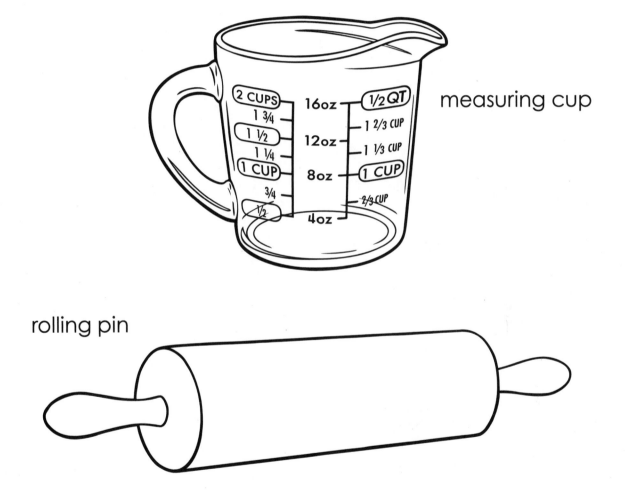

measuring cup

rolling pin

What do bakers make?

bread

muffin

cookies

What do bakers use?

flour

eggs

flour scoop

Firefighters

Draw yourself and a friend here.

What do firefighters wear?

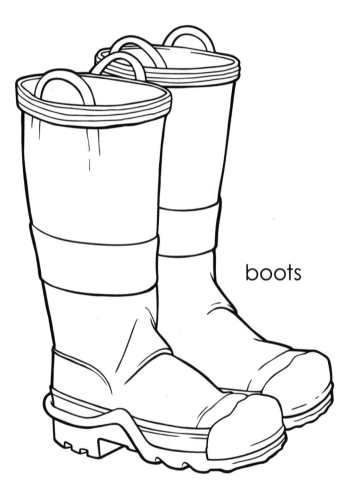

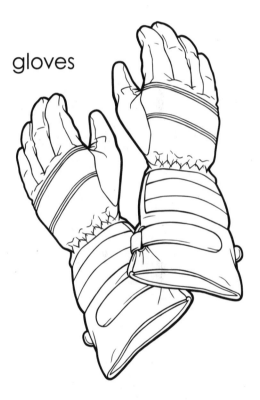

gloves

boots

What do firefighters wear?

hat

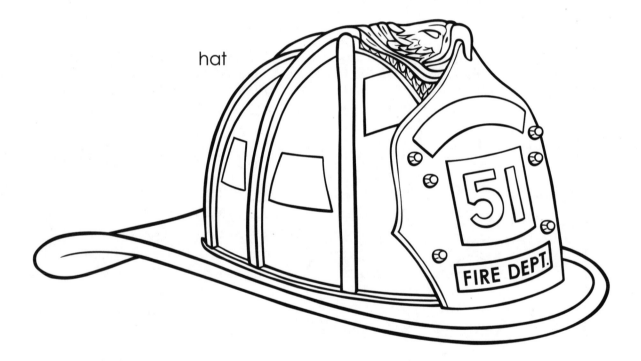

What do firefighters use?

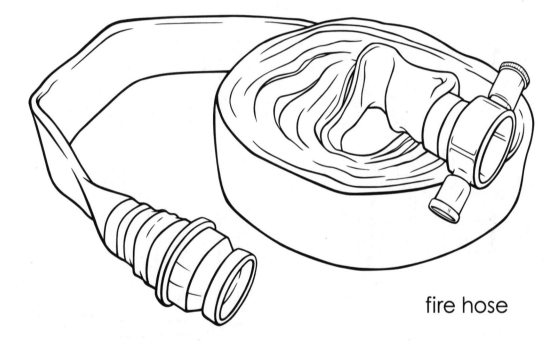

fire hose

Builders

Draw yourself and a friend here.

What do builders wear?

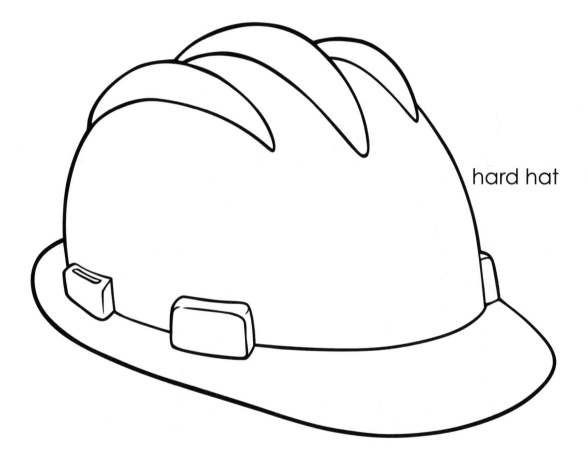

hard hat

What do builders use?

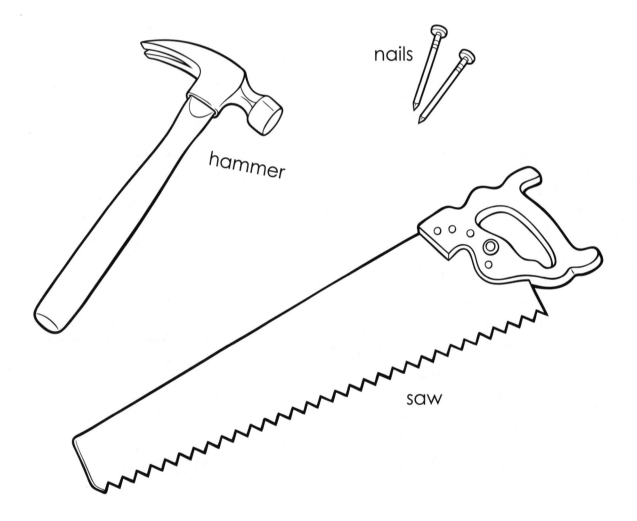

nails

hammer

saw

Grocers

Draw yourself and a friend here.

What do grocers sell?

soup

ketchup

What do grocers sell?

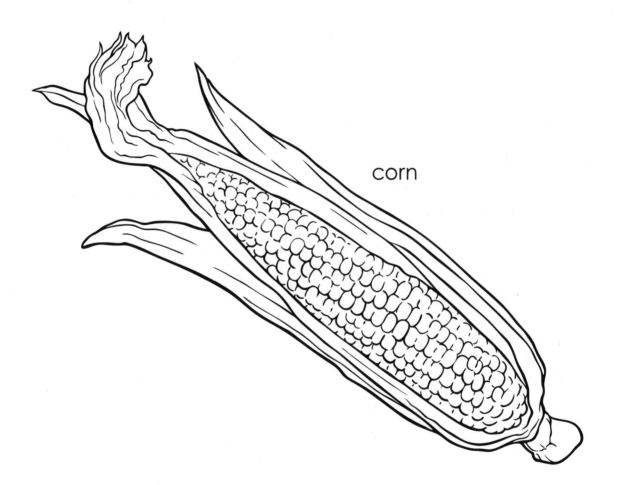

corn

What do grocers sell?

fruit

What do doctors use?

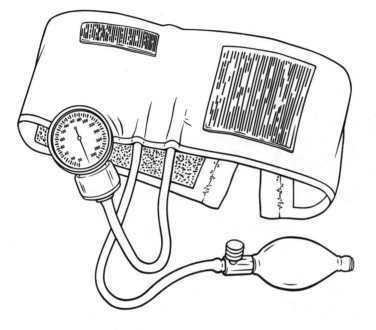

blood pressure cuff

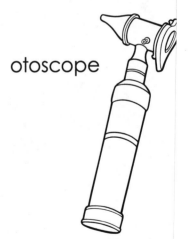

otoscope

What do doctors use?

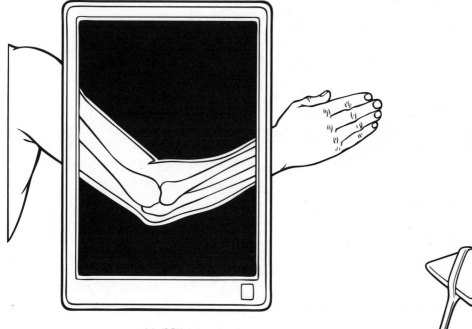

x-ray

reflex hammer

Gardeners

Draw yourself and a friend here.

What do gardeners use?

garden claw

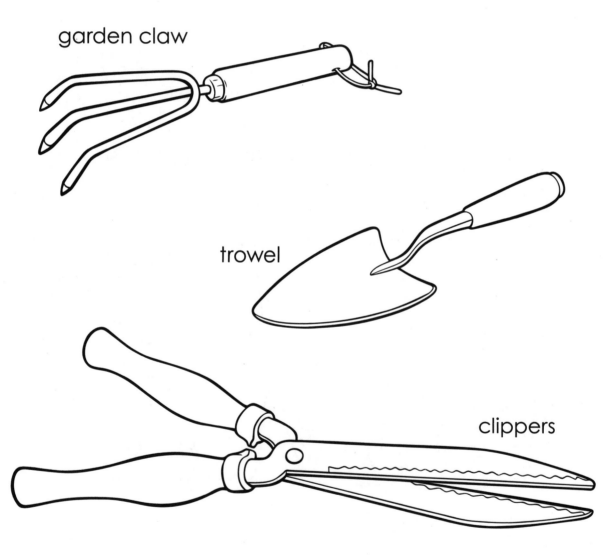

trowel

clippers

What do gardeners use?

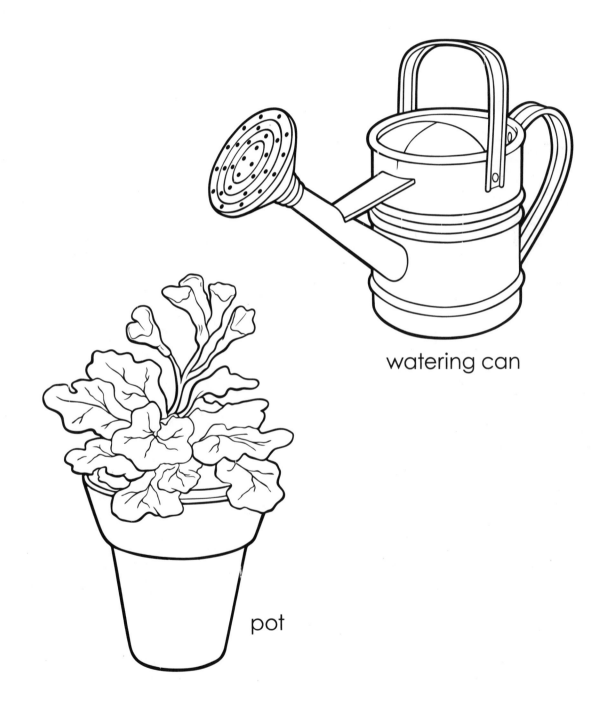

watering can

pot

What do gardeners use?

shovel

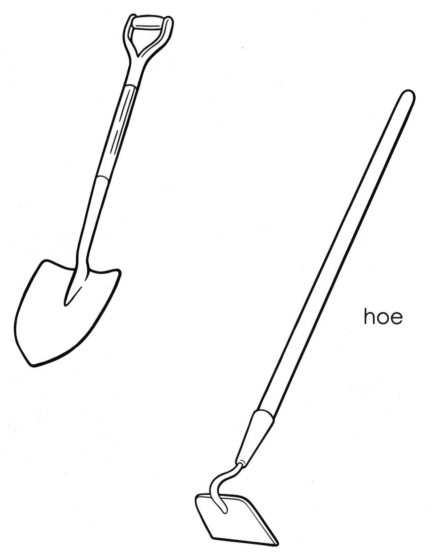

hoe

Police Officers

Draw yourself and a friend here.

What do police officers use?

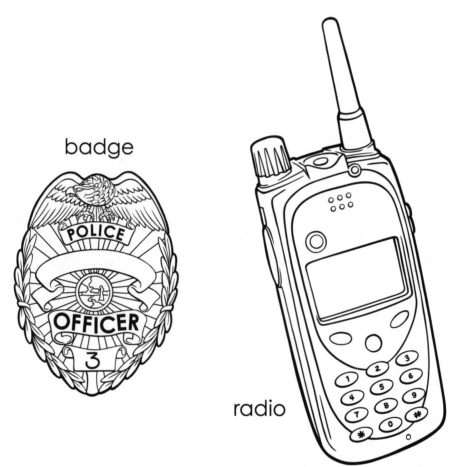

badge

radio

What do police officers wear?

hat

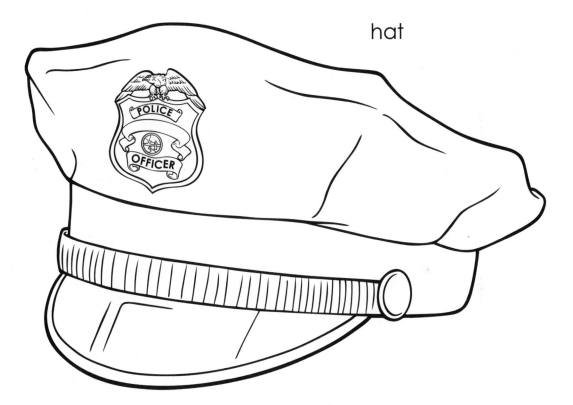

Teachers

Draw yourself and a friend here.

Sometimes a word ends with *–er* or *–or.* That ending is used for words that tell what a person does. Read the poem and circle the words that end with the suffixes *–er* and *–or.* Then draw a picture.

What's My Job?

Sometimes Richard is a singer

And a dancer, too.

Sometimes he's a sailor or

A trainer at the zoo.

Sometimes he's an inventor or

A farmer on a horse.

What is the job that Richard has?

He's an actor, of course!

Draw a house. It can be your house, someone else's, or just one you imagined. Use the small pictures at the top to get ideas.

Draw a picture that shows something your family does together.
Write a sentence about your picture.

_____

_____

_____

_____

Draw your family into the scene.

Draw It

Read a poem about who helps others. Then draw a picture to go with it.

Helping Others

I'll help my little brother
Get dressed when he wakes up.
I'll even feed him mush
And fill his sippy cup!

I'll help my father shop.
I'll set the table too.
And I won't hold my nose
When he serves the stew!

Find It

Inside and Outside

Find all the small pictures in the big picture below.

On the map, find all the items that are shown on the key.

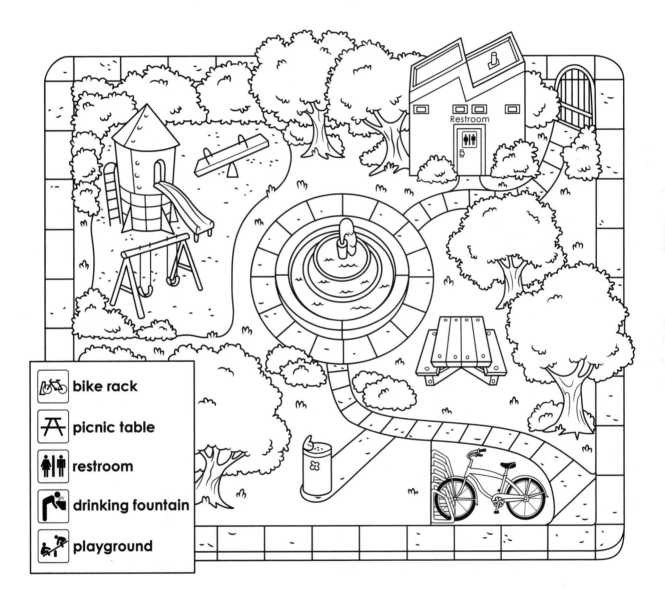

bike rack

picnic table

restroom

drinking fountain

playground

Geography Find It
Neighborhood Map

On the map, find all the items that are shown on the key.

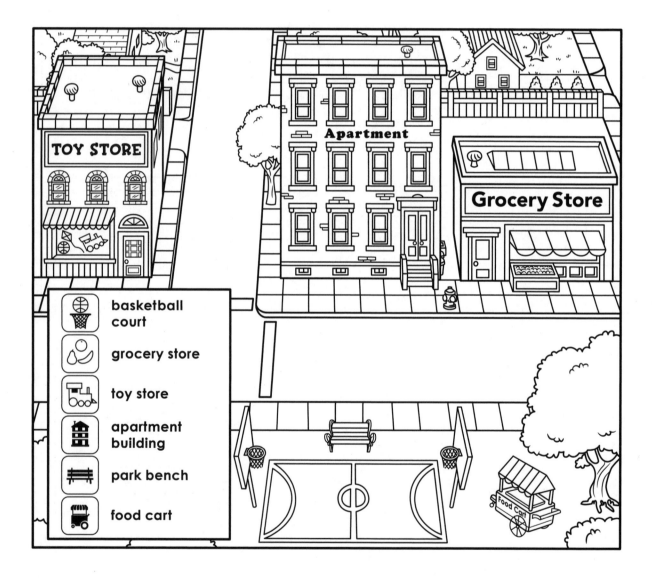

Paragraph Writing
Where do you live?

Carla wrote a paragraph about the place where she lives. Read Carla's paragraph.
Then fill in the blanks to write a paragraph about the place where you live.

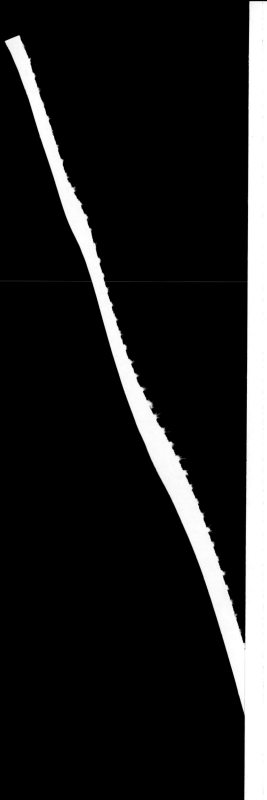

I live in a place called Boulder, and I love it here. My favorite thing to do is go to the mountains because I can play in the snow. I like how the weather is usually sunny. But the best thing about Boulder is that my friends and family are all here.

I live in a place called _____, and I _____ .

My favorite thing to do is _____ because _____ . I like _____ . But the best thing _____ .

Find all the small pictures in the big picture below.

Draw It
Your State

This picture shows things that are found in many states. Draw yourself in the picture and color it. Then write about it.

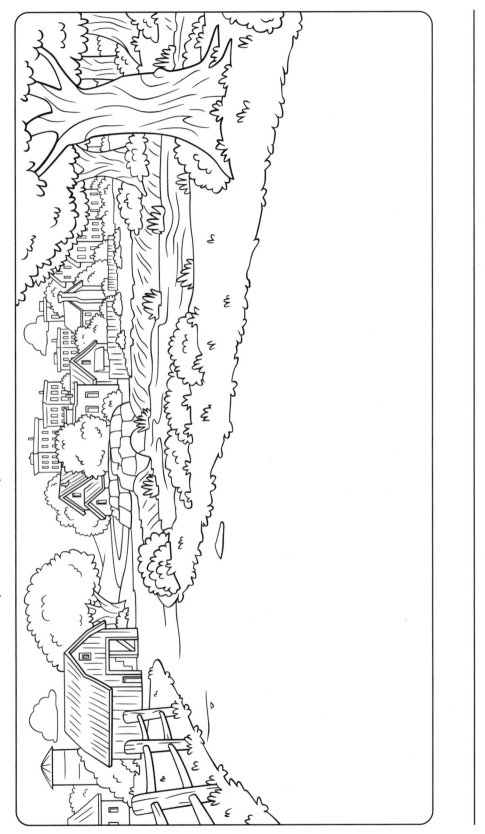

Find all the small pictures in the big picture below.

Draw a map of the place you like to visit. Write a title for your map. Draw symbols on the map. Then make a Map Key.

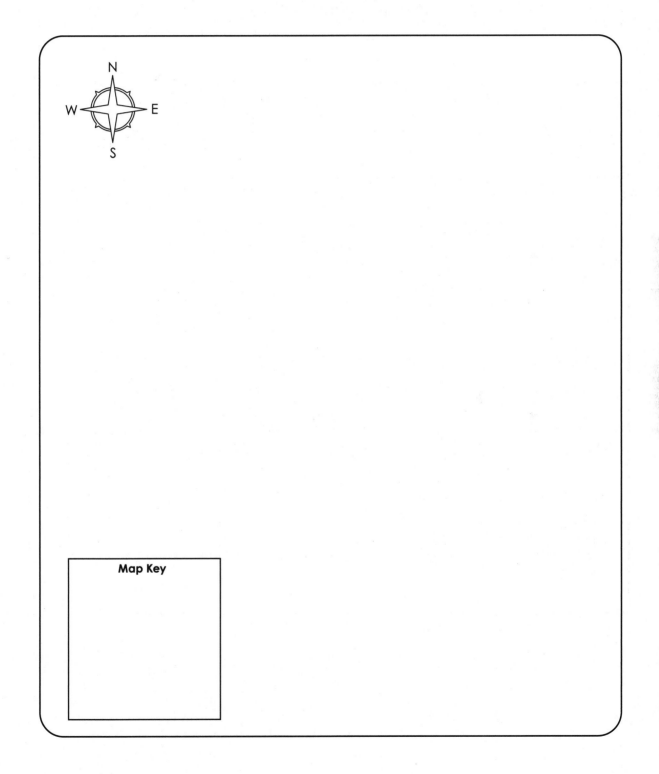

Map Key

Things in the Classroom:
book and pencil

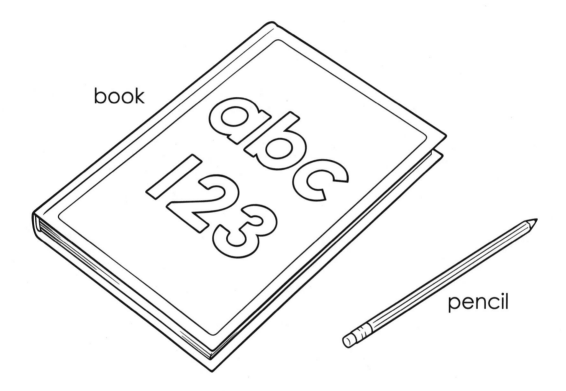

book

pencil

Things in the Classroom:
clock

clock

Things in the Classroom:
desk and computer

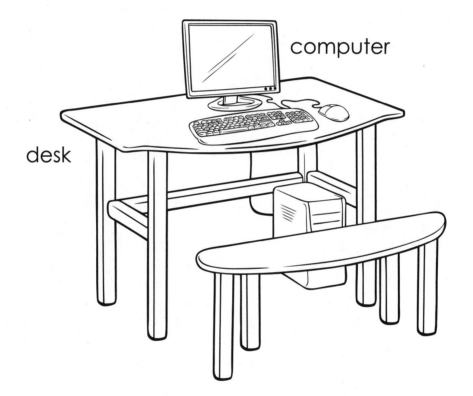

computer

desk

Things in the Classroom:
table and chair

table

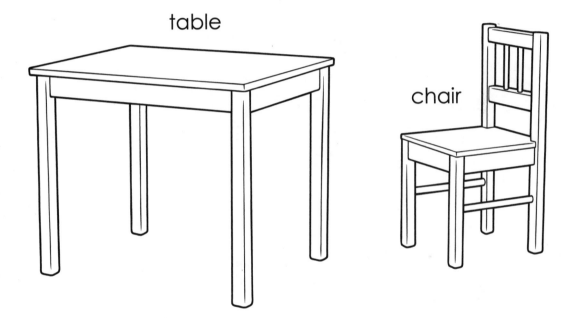

chair

Things in the Kitchen:
bowl of noodles and chopsticks

noodles

bowl

chopsticks

Things in the Kitchen:
bowl of rice and chopsticks

rice

bowl

chopsticks

Things in the Kitchen:
glass and straw

straw

glass

Things in the Kitchen:
plate and cup

cup

plate

Things in the Kitchen:
pot and pan

pot

pan

Things in the Kitchen:
wok

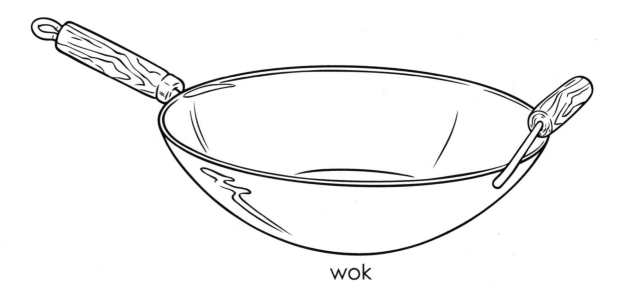

wok

Things in the Kitchen:
spoon

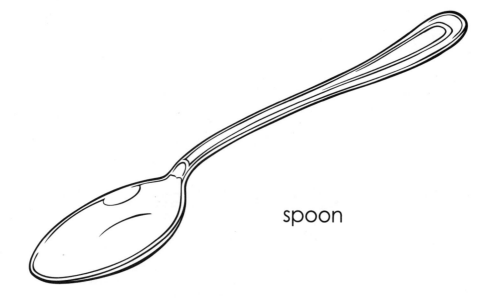

spoon

Things in the Kitchen:
fork

fork

Things in the Kitchen:
knife

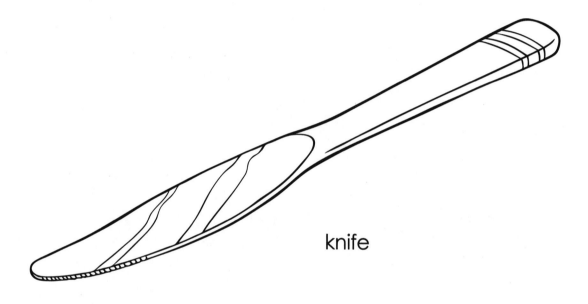

knife

Social Studies Write and Draw
Interview a Family Member

Write an interview question to ask a family member about a belief, value, or tradition that is important to him or her. Ask your question. Draw the answer.

Things in the Bedroom:
bed, pillow, and blanket

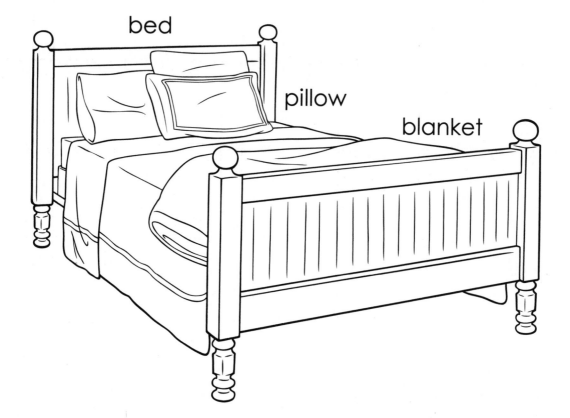

bed

pillow

blanket

Things in the Bedroom:
wall, picture, window, curtains, and clock

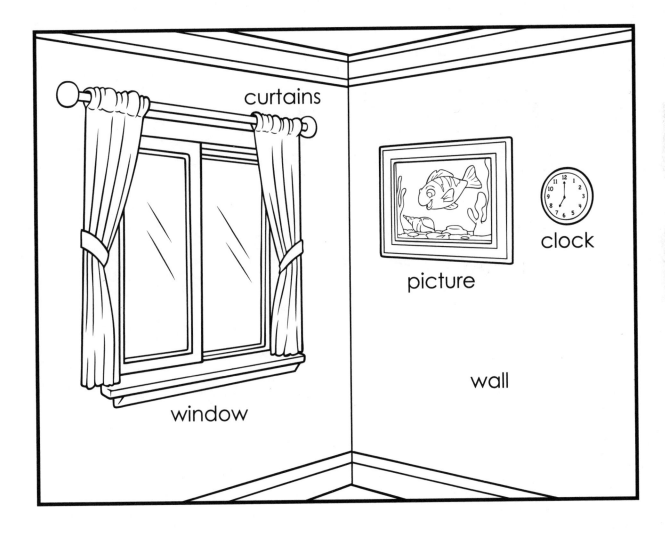

Things in the Bedroom:
desk, chair, lamp, and book

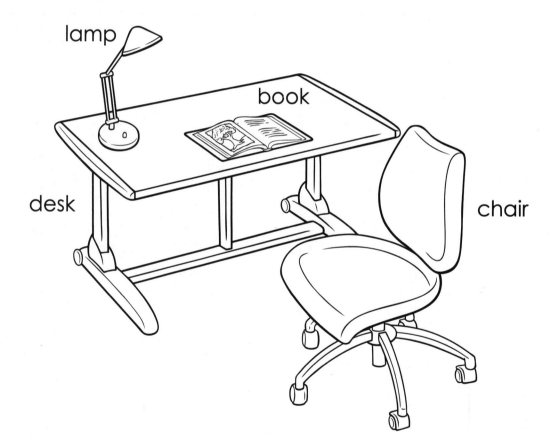

Write and Draw
Timeline: Showing Events

Think of three important things that have happened in your life. On the timeline, draw a picture of each event in the correct order. Write your age for each event below each picture.

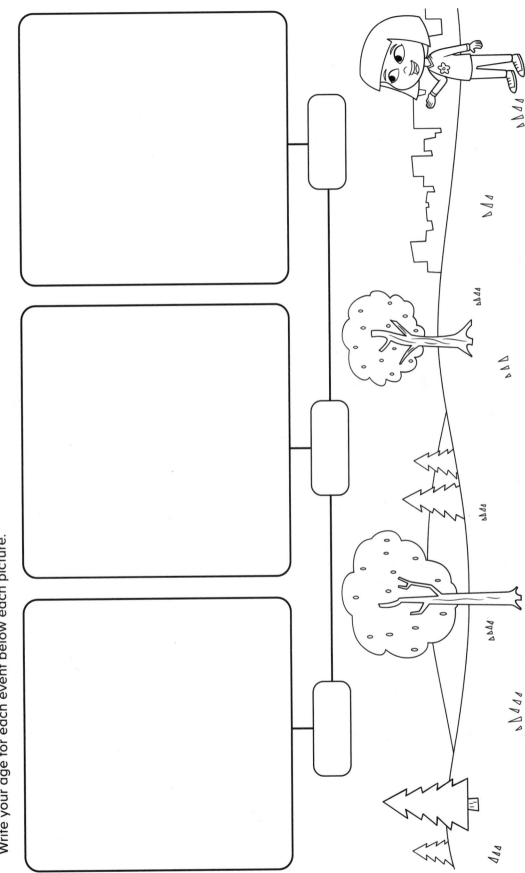

Find It
Garden

Find all the small pictures in the big picture below.

Draw a picture of yourself going on a nature walk. Write about your picture.

Things in the Bedroom:
closet, clothes, shoes, and dresser

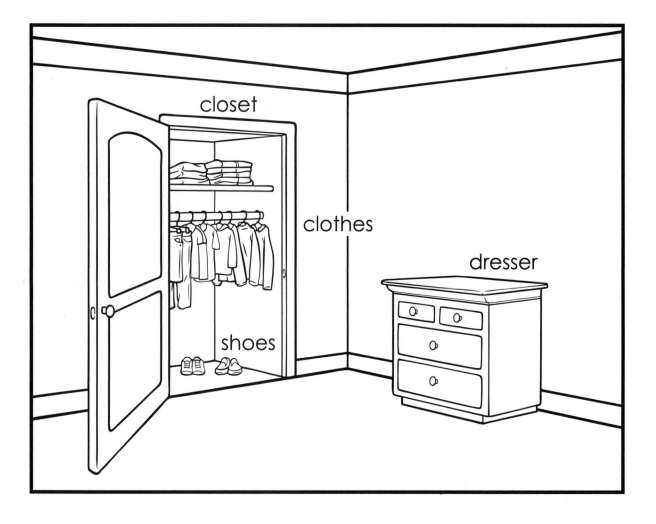

Think about a job you would like to have. Draw a picture of one thing you might do at work. Write about your picture.

Write and Draw
Illustrate a Poem: A Look Around the Library

Read the poem. Write the missing words. Use the word box to help you. Then draw and color a picture to go with the poem.

| around   off   Does   right   read |

A Look Around the Library

Books to the left, books to the _____ —

Which book should I _____ tonight?

My coat comes _____ . I look _____ .

How about this book I found?

_____ *Paper Art* sound good to you?

It does to me, and my mom, too.

One way to show good citizenship in school is to take care of class materials. What is another way to show good citizenship in school? Write about it. Draw a picture.

Find all the small pictures in the big picture below.

Social Studies Crossword
Transportation

Word Box

taxi	car	truck	bus	train	bike	subway	motorcycle	horse

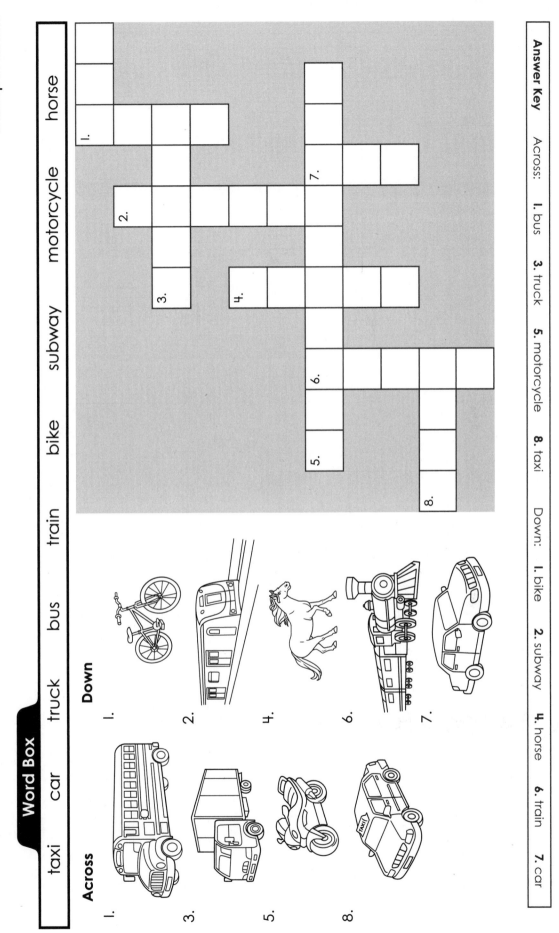

Answer Key

Across: 1. bus 3. truck 5. motorcycle 8. taxi

Down: 1. bike 2. subway 4. horse 6. train 7. car

Down

1.
2.
4.
6.
7.

Across

1.
3.
5.
8.

U is for uniform.

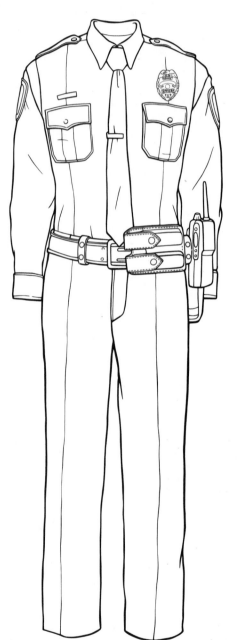